You're
My Hero,

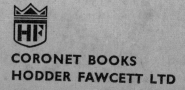

CORONET BOOKS
HODDER FAWCETT LTD

Charlie Brown!

Selected Cartoons from PEANUTS EVERY SUNDAY VOL.2

by CHARLES M. SCHULZ

Copyright © 1958, 1959, 1960, 1961 by United Feature Syndicate, Inc.
First published by Fawcett Publications Inc., New York.
CORONET BOOKS EDITION 1968

SBN 340 04318 0

Printed in Great Britain for Hodder Fawcett Ltd., St. Paul's House,
Warwick Lane, London, E.C.4 by Hazell Watson & Viney Ltd.,
Aylesbury, Bucks

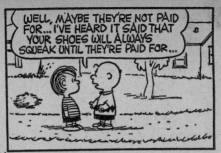

DON'T LET THAT DOG LICK OFF YOUR ICE-CREAM CONE!

ARE YOU CRAZY? DO YOU WANNA GET A BUNCH OF **GERMS**? WHAT'S THE MATTER WITH YOU ANYWAY?

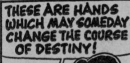

OKAY, CHARLIE BROWN...LET'S GIVE HIM THE OL' FAST ONE... LET'S THROW IT RIGHT BY HIM!

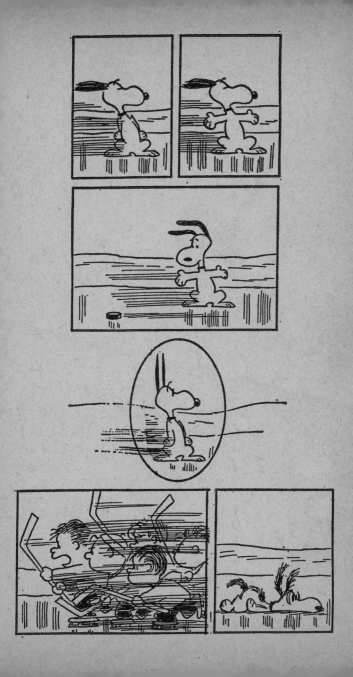

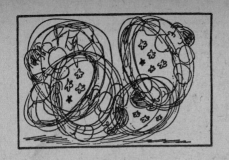

I CAN'T GET THAT STUPID KITE IN THE AIR! I CAN'T! I CAN'T!

OH, COME ON NOW, CHARLIE BROWN...THAT'S NO WAY TO TALK...

THE WHOLE TROUBLE WITH YOU IS YOU DON'T BELIEVE IN YOURSELF! YOU DON'T BELIEVE IN YOUR OWN ABILITIES!

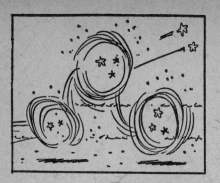

IT ALWAYS COMES AS A SHOCK WHEN IT HAPPENS TO SOMEONE YOU KNOW...

DO YOU WANNA SEE A KID
WITH A GREAT THROWING ARM?

ALL RIGHT, YOU'VE WATCHED THAT PROGRAM LONG ENOUGH!...NOW, I WANT TO WATCH MY PROGRAM!

CLICK

AAUGH!

I CAN'T STAND IT!

WHAT DO YOU HAVE THERE, CHARLIE BROWN?

I'VE WRITTEN A POEM..

REALLY? READ IT..

ALL RIGHT.. IT ISN'T VERY LONG..

SOME DAYS YOU THINK MAYBE YOU KNOW EVERYTHING...SOME DAYS YOU THINK MAYBE YOU DON'T KNOW ANYTHING...SOME DAYS YOU THINK YOU KNOW A FEW THINGS...SOME DAYS YOU DON'T EVEN KNOW HOW OLD YOU ARE.

THAT'S THE WORST POEM I'VE EVER HEARD!

A POEM IS SUPPOSED TO HAVE FEELING! YOUR POEM COULDN'T TOUCH ANYONE'S HEART! YOUR POEM COULDN'T MAKE ANYONE CRY! YOUR POEM COULDN'T..

WAAH!

SOME DAYS YOU THINK MAYBE YOU KNOW EVERYTHING...SOME DAYS YOU THINK MAYBE YOU..

GOOD GRIEF!

SNIF

PERHAPS YOU SHOULD
SEE A DOCTOR...

OH, CUT IT OUT!

WELL, THEY ARE!

WHAT ABOUT THAT LITTLE KID LAST YEAR WHO WOULDN'T SAY HIS PIECE? HE WOULDN'T EVEN GET OFF HIS MOTHER'S LAP! HE WAS SCARED! HE WAS REALLY SCARED!

AND WHAT ABOUT THAT LITTLE BLONDE GIRL WHO STARTED TO CRY WHEN EVERYONE ELSE WAS SINGING? DON'T TELL ME THAT ISN'T WRONG!

I'M REVOLTING AGAINST CHRISTMAS PROGRAMS!!

LOOK...DO YOU SEE THIS? WHAT IS IT?

IT'S MY PART IN THE CHRISTMAS PROGRAM...I'M SUPPOSED TO MEMORIZE IT..

ALL RIGHT...NOW DO YOU SEE THIS? WHAT IS THIS?

IT'S A FIST!

"AND IT CAME TO PASS IN THOSE DAYS, THAT THERE WENT OUT A DECREE FROM CAESAR AUGUSTUS, THAT ALL THE WORLD SHOULD BE TAXED..."

THIS IS A SCULPTURE WHICH STANDS IN THE LITTLE GARDEN JUST BEHIND THE HOUSE..

HERE I AM AGAIN POSING BY THE HOUSE

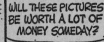
WILL THESE PICTURES BE WORTH A LOT OF MONEY SOMEDAY?

I DOUBT IT..

I DON'T SEE HOW ANYBODY CAN SAVE SOMETHING THAT WON'T BE WORTH A LOT OF MONEY SOMEDAY..

And don't forget about all the other PEANUTS books in the new Fawcett Crest editions. Good Grief! More than 26 million of them in paperback!

© 1967 United Features Syndicate, Inc.

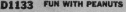

D1097	WHO DO YOU THINK YOU ARE, CHARLIE BROWN?	**D1129**	GOOD GRIEF, CHARLIE BROWN
D1070	GOOD OL' SNOOPY	**D1128**	HEY, PEANUTS!
D1142	VERY FUNNY, CHARLIE BROWN	**D1115**	THE WONDERFUL WORLD OF PEANUTS
D1140	WHAT NEXT, CHARLIE BROWN!	**D1113**	HERE COMES CHARLIE BROWN
D1134	YOU ARE TOO MUCH, CHARLIE BROWN	**D1105**	WE'RE ON YOUR SIDE, CHARLIE BROWN
D1141	FOR THE LOVE OF PEANUTS!	**D1099**	HERE COMES SNOOPY
D1130	YOU'RE A WINNER, CHARLIE BROWN	**D1096**	LET'S FACE IT, CHARLIE BROWN

D1133 FUN WITH PEANUTS

Wherever Paperbacks Are Sold